The Structures and Movement of Breathing

A PRIMER FOR CHOIRS AND CHORUSES

Also available from GIA Publications and Andover Press:

GIA Publications, Inc. (www.giamusic.com)

Evoking Sound by James Jordan

The Musician's Soul by James Jordan

Andover Press (www.bodymap.org):

How to Learn the Alexander Technique: A Manual for Students by Barbara Conable

What Every Musician Needs to Know about the Body by Barbara Conable

The Structures and Movement of Breathing

A PRIMER FOR CHOIRS AND CHORUSES

BARBARA CONABLE

FOREWORD BY JAMES JORDAN

Illustrated by Tim Phelps

GIA Publications, Inc.
Chicago

For my dear friends,

Jenny Floch Efland and Arthur Efland.

ISBN: 1-57999-099-1
Copyright © 2000 by GIA Publications, Inc.
7404 S. Mason Avenue, Chicago, Illinois 60638
www.giamusic.com

Design: Yolanda Durán

Table of Contents

Acknowledgements 6

How to Use This Book...7

Foreword by James Jordan...8

    Use of Body Mapping in the Choral Rehearsal 8

    Suggested Awareness Reminders 10

    Suggested Alignment Reminders 10

    Suggested Breathing Reminders 11

    Conclusion 11

Author Introduction 13

The Structures and Movement of Breathing 15

Skeletal Balance 15

Nasal Passages 16

Mouth...17

Tongue 18

Temporo-mandibular Joints...19

Facial Muscles 20

Lips...22

Muscles of Pharynx 23

Trachea and Esophagus...24

Lungs..26

Ribs...28

Lungs in Context 30

Diaphragm in Context 31

Excursion of the Diaphragm 32

Abdominal and Pelvic Viscera...33

Abdominal Wall 34

Pelvic Floor/Pelvic Diaphragm.......................................38

Coordination of Movement of the Two Diaphragms.......39

Spine 40

Gathering/Lengthening of the Spine 41

Head-Spine Relationship...42

Up and Over..43

Superficial Muscles of the Neck......................................44

Deep Muscles of the Neck 45

About the Author 46

About the Illustrator 47

James Jordan...47

Index...48

Acknowledgements

I am indebted to William Conable for his practical discovery of the Body Map a decade or so ahead of its becoming a frontier in neuroscience, and to Don Zuckerman, breathing teacher extraordinaire, for his insight into the lengthening and gathering of the spine. Thanks, Bill, and thanks, Don.

How to Use This Book

This book should reside in each choral folder. The choral conductor should refer the choir to one illustration during the warm-up period of each rehearsal, beginning always with information concerning alignment, cycling through the book again and again. This repetition and review allows anatomical clarity to accumulate over the months and years, resulting in better singing.

T he work of Barbara Conable provides choral conductors with a potent new tool. Barbara Conable advocates Body Mapping as a way into the perceptions of the singer. The most startling statement I heard her say in my first workshop with her was that "if a singer has the body mismapped, the singer will use the body improperly." The statement made some immediate sense. But, like all teachers, I thought it was directed at my students, and certainly not me. In the short time of thirty minutes, I discovered I had more misconceptions about my body and its structure than I could have ever imagined. And then I thought, "If I have these misconceptions, what about the child in the children's choir, a singer in a high school choir, my own college students and people in countless church and community choirs, what are they thinking?"

Body Mapping allows conductors to give bits and pieces of anatomical truth to the choir each rehearsal, both during the choral warm-up and during the rehearsal. These bits accumulate over time into a potent arsenal of information that will allow people to sing at their maximum potential. If one reconstructs the rehearsal paradigm to include movement truths, then one's singers are constantly empowered to make incredible sounds within bodies that are aligned. Choirs sing with more rhythmic excitement because rhythmic impulses are not short-circuited by rigid muscular holding. As an added benefit, the conductor whose own body is correctly mapped will discover a freer conducting gesture that results in heightened breathing and listening skills.

USE OF BODY MAPPING IN THE CHORAL REHEARSAL

The choral warm-up has assumed many functions: a time for refocusing and pitch sensitivity, a time to give pedagogical helps and reminders to the choir, and a time in which, through a litany of exercises, the choir is readied to sing. I believe Body Mapping to be one of the most effective tools to that end.

Body Mapping does not use postural language. In fact, postural language should be eliminated from the rehearsal. "Stand up straight," "shoulders down and around and back" are phrases from the posture jargon that lead to body misuse. Why? Because they cause one to readjust one's body muscularly and hold it in an unnatural position. Body buoyancy is thereby compromised and vocal freedom is severely hampered. Barbara Conable is advocating, as am I, the inoculation of our choirs against the posture virus. In order to avoid rigid and unnatural positions, conductors should not use the term *posture,* but rather the word *alignment.* Correct alignment is facilitated in this Body Mapping approach through anatomical knowledge.

Alignment should now come to mean understanding and correcting one's own Body Map so that one's body can find its balanced and efficient "place" for singing. If one believes that breath is central to the singing process, then it should follow that the "container" for that breath must be re-prepared every rehearsal for the breath needed for singing. Singers come into rehearsal breathing for their daily life. Breathing for singing requires a different container that is free of muscular tension. That container must be reconstructed or re-visualized each rehearsal before breath exercises and singing take place or conductors risk a wrath of

tone, pitch and rhythm problems that find their roots in misalignment.

Each warm-up, the choir should examine illustrations in this octavo. This should be done first in the warm-up process, just after vigorous stretching, using these books that are in each folder. If singers perceive their bodies correctly, in an anatomical sense, they will use their bodies correctly. If they do not perceive them correctly, they will use their bodies in the way they perceive them. Several minutes each rehearsal should be devoted to viewing the illustrations. After a period of time, there will be a healthy accumulation of correct maps in the singers' minds. It is then the job of the conductor during the rehearsal to give short verbal cues to recall the information needed. This should become a rehearsal technique. For example, "Choir, as you sing that forte phrase, remember that your spines are lengthening, not shortening." (p. 43) When dealing with a diction problem, remind the choir not to form consonants and vowels with their "lipstick lips," but rather with the larger muscular structure that is the "movement lips." (p. 22) "Relax the tongue" has new meaning when the choir has mapped the tongue and realizes its enormous size! (p. 18) "Float the ribs" has new meaning when one understands the dynamic flexibility of the ribs! (p. 29) Give your choir "a piece of the truth" every rehearsal. I can assure you that if this information is used as we suggest, your choir will sing with a new vibrancy and freedom that will bring excitement into every rehearsal.

SUGGESTED AWARENESS REMINDERS

Like it or not, choral conductors must understand that singers have found it extremely difficult to monitor both their singing and their bodies during a choral rehearsal. When surrounded by sound, singers often turn outward rather than inward to their own perceptions. Hence, their singing becomes external. A primary rehearsal rule should be to keep the choir in an awakened state both spiritually and mentally.

Constant verbal reminders concerning singers' awareness are of central importance in the rehearsal. In a private voice lesson, the voice teacher assumes the role of alignment monitor. As soon as a student becomes misaligned or unaware, the teacher perceives it and gives the appropriate correction. However, due to the group dynamic of the choral rehearsal, singers may lose touch with their bodies, that is, become perceptually unaware of their bodies, without correction. They become perceptually numb. The following phrases will re-awaken their experience of themselves:

- *Sing with your whole body, please.*

- *Are you aware of your breathing?*

- *How are your ribs moving as you sing?*

- *As you sustain the phrase, are your spines lengthening?*

- *Are you keeping your heads independent and mobile?*

- *Are you thinking Up and Over?*

- *How is the joint of your head to your spine? Is it free? Can you sense it?*

SUGGESTED ALIGNMENT REMINDERS

As part of the regular rehearsal process, it is important to keep important principles forefront in the singers' minds. Consistent reinforcement of principles is, perhaps, the single most important teaching tool that a conductor has. In fact, it is my experience that reinforcement of these principles is the single most important ingredient to a healthy, in-tune and vibrant choral sound. Below are a group of ideas which should be continually reinforced during the course of a rehearsal:

- *Remember your weight-bearing spine, at your core.*

- *Are you balanced at your hip joints?*

- *Are your knees released and flexible?*

- *Are your feet feeling the floor?*

- *Are you feeling the tripod of your feet's arches?*

- *Are your heads dynamically poised?*

- *Are your backs free? Long and wide?*

- *Remember to organize around your spine like an apple around a core.*

- *When you look down at your music, just tilt your head. Don't drag your neck forward.*

- *Remember to balance your arms. Don't pull them back, or slump them down.*

SUGGESTED BREATHING REMINDERS

A singer's Body Map of breathing also needs consistent reinforcement. Verbal cues can be used:

- *Breathing moves from the top down, not like a glass filling up.*

- *Remember, breathing moves in the body in a wave, from top to bottom.*

- *Breathe through your front tube (trachea) not the back tube (esophagus).*

- *Breathe leaving your swallowing muscles alone.*

- *When you breathe, your ribs do not expand, they make outward and inward excursions.*

- *You breathe at breathing joints, and those breathing joints are in the back.*

- *When you take air in, your spine gathers, like a cat preparing to spring.*

- *When you are using air to sing, your spine lengthens, like a cat springing.*

- *Remember what space your lungs occupy in your chest cavity.*

- *Your diaphragm works on inhalation. Leave the area alone to dome back up on exhalation.*

- *Experience the whole cylinder of your abdominal wall.*

- *Outward and downward release allows your spine to lengthen.*

CONCLUSION

It has been my experience that no single factor more affects the quality of choral sound than alignment. Poor alignment tends to grow insidiously within the choral rehearsal if it is not kept in check by the conductor. While the principles presented above and in this booklet appear to be rather simple, they are pedagogically potent. In fact, I would say that without accurate Body Maps and sensory awareness, it is difficult, if not impossible, to obtain a truly out-standing choral sound.

If one uses these principles, the choral tone will achieve a new vibrancy and resonance heretofore unheard within the ensemble. I will warn both conductors and singers, however, that this work must be done in every rehearsal. The conductor must become vigilant and be an advocate for alignment, without which the ensemble will labor unnecessarily to sing.

There is a saying among teachers: what is usually easiest learned is hardest taught. Alignment principles are easily acquired, but require constant vigilance by the conductor. I believe that the materials that follow will make that objective reachable for choirs of all levels.

The purpose of this book is to give choristers clear and adequate information about their breathing so that they may sing with optimal enjoyment and beauty. Excellent singers' breathing depends on three conditions: freedom from tension throughout the body, a lively, on-going body awareness, and an accurate Body Map (or "internal representation," as some scientists call it) of the structures and movement of breathing.

The purpose of this book is to provide a context for vocal technique rather than technique itself. Vocal technique varies greatly across styles of choral singing, but the context for each style is the same. Body awareness, an adequate and accurate Body Map, and freedom from tension serve the members of a jazz choir as well as they serve a cathedral choir or a gospel choir, though the members are singing with different techniques.

Body awareness is essential to good singing. We must perceive clearly and sufficiently the movement of our own singing, including our breathing. Perception of the movement of our singing comes to us from our kinesthetic sense, which also tells us about our body's position and our size. Kinesthetic sensations arise from specialized sense organs in our muscles. In other words, we have "smart" muscles, as well as "smart" ears and eyes. We also have smart skin, rich with the tactile information singers need.

In addition to kinesthetic and tactile awareness, singers need full experience of their own emotions and the emotions inspired by the music they're singing. All this inner awareness, together with auditory and visual information, is called inclusive awareness. Inclusive awareness contains all relevant information in the moment the information is needed. Inclusive awareness is a rich and pleasurable state of being, one of the reasons people love singing so much. As a bonus, inclusive awareness and an accurate Body Map are effective proof against problems that plague singers, truly protecting singers over a lifetime.

Our Body Maps are our physical self-representations. We literally map our own bodies with our brains, that is, we conceive neurally what we're like (structure), what we do (function), and how big we are (size). We map our whole bodies in this regard, and we map their parts. If our Body Maps are accurate we move well. If our Body Maps are inconsistent with the reality of our structures we do not move well. Singing is movement, and its quality is as determined by our Body Maps as the quality of our walking is. Fortunately, inaccurate or inadequate Body Maps can be replaced with accurate and adequate Body Maps. All that is needed is information and attention to information. Human beings are naturally self-correcting, and our Body Maps are no exception. When singers return to the richness of their own sensations, and when they apprehend and honor their actual structures, they find balance, freedom and, with practice, mastery.

Profound embodiment is also the key to ensemble. Singers' continuous, intimate, often intense awareness of their own bodies (sensations, movements, and emotions) is the ideal condition for feeling and responding to each other and to the conductor. Then a chorus is a chorus and not just a collection of individuals singing at the same time. The many choral conductors who have helped their singers regain full body awareness as they sing are surprised and delighted by the terrific difference embodiment makes in the quality of the singing.

Among the many benefits of singing is the spilling over into daily life of the skills singing perfects: body awareness carries into washing the dishes; the Body Map that informs sitting comfortably to rehearse informs sitting comfortably at the computer; the cultivated freedom for singing becomes also freedom for hiking and playing tennis. This creates a virtuous circle in which singing enhances life, and life enhances singing. Then one lives, in the words of W.A. Mathieu, "the musical life."

The Structures and Movement of Breathing

When we sing well we sing with our whole bodies, which are supported and organized centrally around our spines. We may perceive balance and poise around our spines using our lively, on-going body awareness. Within our bodies we may feel **(1)** the balance of our heads on our spines, at the center; we may feel **(2)** the balance of our arm structures over our spines, at the center; we may feel **(3)** the balance of our thorax on our massive lumbar vertebrae, at the center; we may feel **(4)** the balance of our upper half over our legs, at the center; we may feel **(5)** the balance at our knees, at the center; and we may feel **(6)** the balance of our bodies on the arches of our feet, at the center.

skeletal balance

The enemies of balance are "standing up straight" and slouching. "Standing up straight" is rigid, pulled up and back, off the spine; slouching is pulled down and in, off the spine. By analogy to pitch, standing up straight is sharp and slouching is flat. If we are pulled up or pulled down we may move back to balance or poise as we would move back to pitch from sharp or flat. Balance around our weight-bearing, weight-delivering spines and legs is the best postural condition for singing. Our singing structures are supported by our bony architecture and our superficial muscles are free to gesture beautifully.

This book explores the structures and movement of breathing, beginning at the top, progressing downward through the torso, and then, full circle, back to the spine and head, remembering the whole as we explore the parts, as we do with music. ▨

Our breathing brings air into our bodies through our nasal passages or our mouths. As singers we match the amount of air taken in to the phrase that follows the inhalation. This is a skill singers develop over time, sometimes unconsciously. We learn to know quite precisely how much air we have, a judgment we make with our senses. Nasal passages are lined with sense receptors, so, just as we may feel a breeze on our faces with our skin, we may feel the movement of air within our nasal passages. This is important information, not to be missed.

We must not limit ourselves by mapping the nasal area as merely facial. We need to "think nose" all the way back to the pharynx, allowing our sensations in this area, including the sometimes quite intense sensations of vibration, to give us an increasingly complete apprehension of this interior area and the air that flows through it. ▨

n a s a l   p a s s a g e s

Our mouths, like our noses, are rich with sensory information. Our mouths are the beginning of our digestive systems, which include also the pharynx, esophagus, stomach and intestines. Because the mouth is a nutrient-receiving structure as well as an air-receiving structure, the more common use of sense receptors here is gaining information about the movement of food and drink, but these receptors need to be recruited for singing as well. The way connoisseurs appreciate the texture of food and wine, canny singers savor air and movement in their mouths, learning from the sensation.

Tactile receptors continually offer information about the location of our sensitive surfaces, defining our

boundaries, in this case, the palate, tongue, cheeks, lips, and gums. In addition, tactile receptors offer information about anything that touches the skin, in this case, air. This economy is nature's way.

Our oral space is bounded by the roof of the mouth above, the muscular floor of the mouth below, the muscular facial cheeks at the sides, and the tongue within, so the mouth is not a thing but rather a space among things! It must be mapped this way! In singing, the space is radically altered again and again by the structures that form it and fill it. The movement must be mapped as movements of the structures that form the space, not as a function of the space itself. ▨

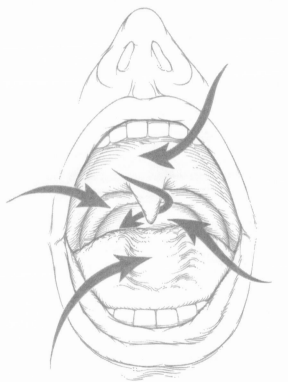

mouth

A newborn's tongue is entirely in its mouth. Years of maturation alter the configuration of the mouth and throat so that an adult's tongue is secured at its base just above the larynx and hyoid bone, in the throat. Fully a third of the tongue's length is vertical in an adult, forming a portion of the front of the throat. It is essential to map the full depth of the tongue into the throat, the full width of the tongue, in the throat and in the mouth, and its full length, in order to insure the tongue's dexterity.

Most muscles in the body move bones, but some singing muscles simply move themselves, among them our tongue. Our tongue's movements are complex, a function of the complexity of the fiber structure. The very precise map of the tongue a singer needs may be developed over time by the use of kinesthetic and tactile receptors to feel its varied movement and its edges. Moving the tongue with awareness helps us to map it precisely; mapping the tongue helps us to free it; freeing it helps us to move it well in singing. A virtuous circle! �

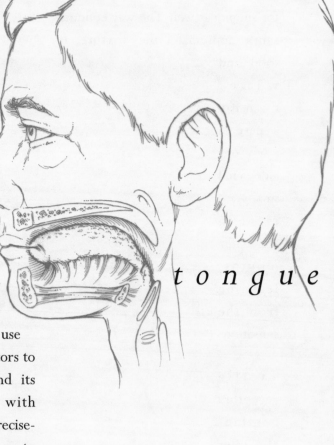

tongue

The jaw is an appendage to the skull, a separate anatomical unit, and it moves in relation to the skull by virtue of our two temporo-mandibular joints. The temporo-mandibular joints (TMJs) are the joints of the mandible (the jawbone) and the skull at the base of the temples. Singers must map a single jaw in relation to the skull, NOT JAWS. Singers with JAWS in their Body Maps attempt to open their mouths in both directions as if they had both an upper jaw and a lower jaw, instead of simply swinging their one jaw down. Their attempt to open in both directions unnecessarily involves the whole head and neck in what should be a simple, local movement at the TMJs. One jaw. Two TMJs.

Our TMJs are just in front of our ears, not behind them, as some people think, nor at the forward protuberances which slide along our cheekbones, nor just behind the teeth, nor at the bumps near the bottom of the ear lobes. These common mismappings cause forced, tense, strange movement of the jaw plus pain and injury in the joints for some people. Each mismapping causes a different misuse of the jaw, each one injurious to free singing. As soon as singers map the structure accurately the movement becomes free and efficient. This is an instance of "the truth shall make you free," and of the corrective power of a changed Body Map. ※

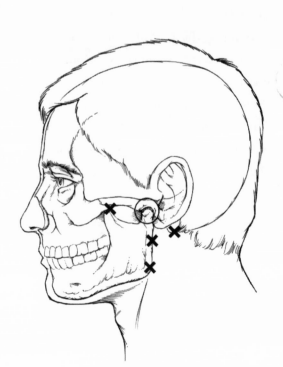

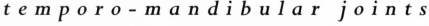

t e m p o r o - m a n d i b u l a r   j o i n t s

These are the muscles of the face, some of which contribute to the shaping of vowels and the articulating of consonants. Their larger contribution to singing is appropriate facial expression. Facial muscles, along with other gestures from other parts of the body, accomplish the dramatic part of singing, the looks of love, ecstasy, suffering, delight, and the rest. Different styles of choral singing allow for more or less facial expression among the singers, but even among the very broad facial gestures of barbershop choruses, mugging must be avoided, as must deadpan with more facially subdued styles.

A common confusion between cheek muscles and soft palate must be avoided. Many singers manipulate their cheeks when they mean to use their soft palate for the creation of certain sounds. For some singers, the palate rises as the cheeks rise, but this confusion gives singers a Cheshire Cat look almost always at odds with the meaning of the music. Clarifying the Body Map is the only remedy, returning the face to its full range of facial expression and freeing singers to use the soft palate as their technique requires, independent of the face.

We may acquaint ourselves with our facial muscles by consciously inventing or imitating facial expressions, noticing the independence of facial muscles from mouth and throat muscles. We may acquaint ourselves with our palate by using mirrors, or by palpating the tissue with our tongues, or with our thumbs, distinguishing the bony roof of the mouth (the hard palate) from the soft tissue behind it, or by consulting the technique manuals that instruct singers in the proper use of the soft palate. With instruction and practice, our soft palate may be fully appreciated kinesthetically, as it moves, carrying out the techniques of singing.

Full facial expression is also lost in the raising of facial muscles as the pitch rises and the lowering of facial muscles as the pitch lowers, causing facial gestures of alternate astonishment and dejection no matter what the emotional content of the music. The remedy is a clear distinction in our Body Maps between facial muscles and pitch producing structures. ▩

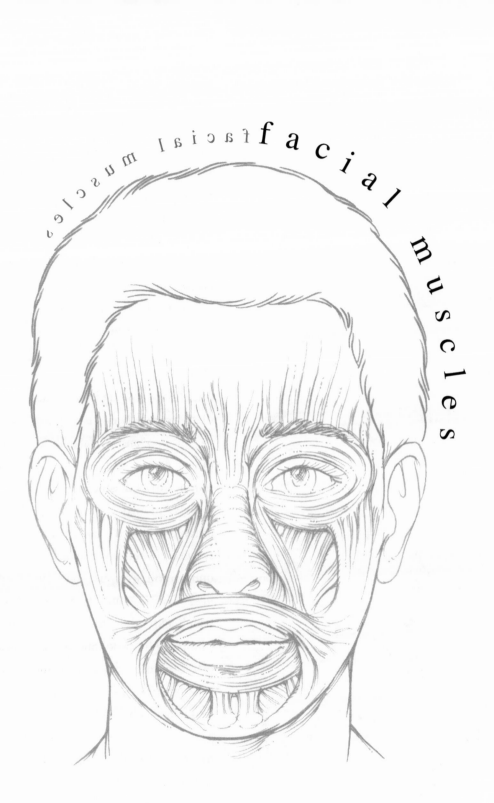

lips *lips* *lips* *lips* **lips**

Choral music is sung poetry or prayer. The text is significant, and the words are an essential part of the artistic whole. Therefore, Polyhymnia, Muse of Choral Singing, is displeased when her words can't be understood by the audience. She frowns and frets. Indistinct words result from two causes: undervalued consonants (the audience doesn't want to hear just vowels!) and mismapping of lips.

Our lips are very important facial muscles for singing because they articulate frequently occurring consonants like m, b, p, and w, partially articulate others like f and v, and lips move significantly for other consonants and vowels. In order to accomplish the extensive and rapid movement required of the lips if words are to be understood we must map our whole lips, that is, our "movement lips," which extend from cheek to cheek (dimple to dimple) and from the base of the nose to the base of the gums. Our "lipstick lips" are merely specialized skin cells exterior to a small portion of the movement lips. Trying to sing with the lipstick lips ruins articulation and the shaping of vowels. Singing with the whole muscle perfects articulation. Polyhymnia smiles. ▨

Air enters through our nasal and oral spaces by virtue of the muscular action of the intercostal muscles (between the ribs) and by the diaphragm, triggered by the brain based on information from chemoreceptors in the blood vessels and brain, or, in the case of singing, by intention. The behavior of air itself is a factor, air moving, as it does, from areas of higher density to areas of lower density. From the nose or mouth, air passes within the pharnygeal space, into the trachea, bronchia, and lungs. The pharyngeal space is bounded by the base of the tongue and the pharyngeal muscles, and it is the part of the alimentary canal between the mouth and the esophagus. It is of supreme importance for singers to map the pharyngeal muscles as part of the digestive system. Nature simply gets double duty from this space, as from the mouth, using it for both nutrients and air. The muscles of the pharynx are active with regard to food and

drink; they swallow food and drink. Air does not need to be swallowed, and pharyngeal muscles are not active in bringing in air, unless their function is mismapped. Some singers tighten pharyngeal muscles, believing them to be inhaling muscles, resulting in audible inhaling because of the constriction in the pharyngeal space. When singers correctly map the area as digestive, not respiratory, they no longer constrict on inhalation. They inhale quietly, and as quickly as they need. ▨

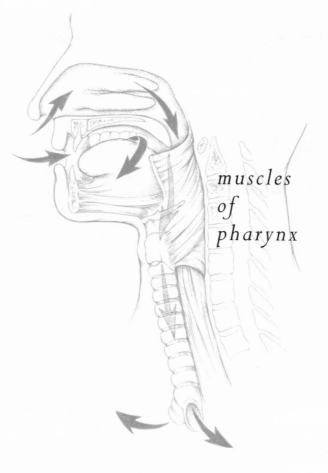

muscles of pharynx

The trachea, often called the windpipe, lying just under the skin in the front of our lower necks, is merely a passageway for air on inhalation. On exhalation, however, its specialized top portion, the larynx, which contains the vocal cords, interrupts air, if we choose, and sets air vibrating, resulting in singing or speaking or any of the other myriad sounds we are capable of making.

The esophagus, lying behind the trachea, is the food tube. Singers with tight throats will almost always describe or draw the esophagus as lying in front of the trachea. Their descriptions and their drawings reveal the mistake in their Body Map that creates their tension. Mapping the air tube accurately, in front of the food tube, resolves the tension.

The common and very destructive confusion concerning the location of the trachea and esophagus and the function of the pharyngeal muscles is often accompanied by a misunderstanding of sound, which is that sound is a substance, something that a singer may, for instance, "project." Singers with substance fantasies are prone to use the food-moving apparatus to sing. Sound is not a substance; it is merely and purely vibration in air. Singers who comprehend this fact fully move air cleanly in and out through the trachea, using their intercostals and their diaphragms. The esophagus waits there behind the trachea for something good to eat after the rehearsal. ▦

trachea trachea trachea trachea trachea trachea trachea trachea trachea

trachea

trachea   esophagus

Here are drawings of the lungs, features of the human body which a singer should know intimately, for air is brought into the multiple tubes of the lungs in order to offer its supply of vital oxygen to the blood at the interface of the respiratory and circulatory systems. Singers recycle, so to speak, the spent, waste-laden air by setting its molecules vibrating at pleasing frequencies on its way back out into the world. This opportunistic, improbable recruiting of one function for another should be celebrated. Human beings turn exhaust into song!

Our lungs, plus our heart, occupy the thoracic cavity, the space above the diaphragm, which is roughly the upper half of the rib area in front, and somewhat lower in back. We need utter clarity about the location of our lungs. The tops of our lungs are above our collarbones, the bottoms of our lungs near the lower tip of the sternum (the breastbone). Any fantasy that lungs are below the thoracic cavity will result in effort and distortion in breathing.

Our lungs lie under our upper ribs in back, and our shoulder blades lie over these ribs, serving as lung shields. Without the protection of shoulder blades and ribs the lungs would be more vulnerable to puncture. We may effectively map the location of our lungs by moving our shoulder blades in all directions on our upper backs and noting that everywhere the shoulder blades go there is lung underneath. ▨

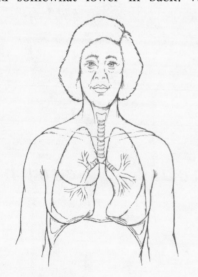

lungs from the front

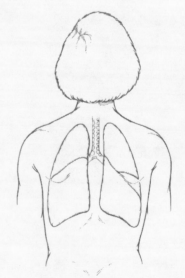

lungs from the back

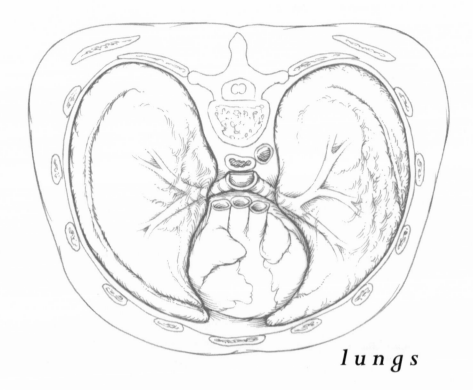

lungs

In this picture, the lungs are shown in relation to thoracic vertebrae. Many singers limit and distort their breathing by imagining their lungs lie forward of their spine. In fact, at least half our air comes into the portions of our lungs that lie alongside our spine. The frequent injunction to "breathe into the back" is therefore anatomically correct. We are constructed to breathe into our backs, literally.

This example illustrates a principle: the more concrete singers are in their thinking and perceiving, the better they sing. If we say, "I will breathe into my back," we are speaking abstractly, as people do who say, "I will breathe into my sprained ankle to make it feel better." The statement "I will breathe into my back" may arouse the imagination more than it arouses sensory perception. By contrast, if we say, "I will seek to perceive clearly the movement that brings air alongside my weight-bearing spine and within my moving ribs," we are speaking with a kind of specificity that continually enhances our body awareness and refines our Body Map, freeing our imaginations for the music. We don't imagine our bodies; we perceive them! ◼

We have twenty-four ribs, twelve on each side, twenty meeting springy cartilage in front and all meeting the spine in back, where each rib attaches to a transverse process on one of the twelve thoracic vertebrae. This means that we breathe at twenty-four breathing joints in back, a breathing joint being where each rib moves in relation to the spine as we inhale and exhale. Each rib swings up and out in relation to the spine as we inhale, and each rib swings down and in as we exhale. This swinging up and out, down and in, accounts for what scientists call the "excursion" of the ribs, a much better word than the more common word "expansion," because ribs do not expand in the usual sense of the word. Ribs move at joints, like all other bones, by the action of muscles, in this case, the muscles that lie between the ribs, called the intercostals. One set of intercostal muscles moves the ribs up and out and another set moves the ribs down and in. Excursion, of course, correlates with volume of air inhaled.

The movement of all twenty-four ribs can be clearly felt, monitored, and controlled. We rarely need maximum capacity in singing, but when we do, only totally free moving ribs will acquire it. On exhalation a singer may control the descent of the ribs so they make a long, slow, even excursion across a long phrase. It is this control which differentiates breathing while singing from ordinary breathing. Both are natural, but one is controlled by intention and the other is controlled by the brain's response to messages from the blood. The chemoreceptors which ordinarily determine the amount of inhaled air do not know when we want to sing a long tone! ▩

r i b s ,   b a c k   v i e w

Singing is movement. Breathing is movement. Rib movement is an important part of the whole movement of breathing. Ribs move at joints in back, but ribs move at cartilage in front. Each of the ribs attached to the sternum is attached by an expanse of cartilage between the ribs and the sternum that allows for rib movement because of its springy texture. Our lower ribs, except for our four floating ribs, are attached to each other by cartilage. We may palpate the cartilage and feel its texture. We may contrast the relative hardness of the sternum and ribs with the springiness of the cartilage under our fingers. We may lay our hands along the cartilage and feel the movement of the springy cartilage in breathing, and we may contrast the cartilage movement with the swinging up and out, down and in, of the ribs. Partly by virtue of the cartilage we deepen front to back as we inhale, and we widen side to side.

Rib movement is crucial to life, and rib movement is crucial to singing. Rib movement must be distinguished from the heaving up and down of the thorax at vertebral joints, a movement of the thorax we can make while we inhale, while we exhale, and while we hold our breath, proving it is a movement unrelated to breathing. Breathing happens not at vertebral joints, as heaving and collapsing do, but at the joints of our

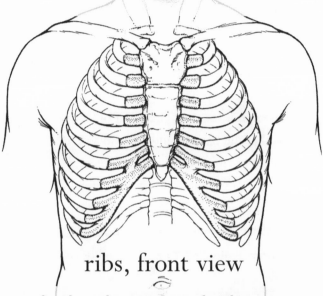

ribs, front view

ribs with our spines and at the cartilage. Rib movement must also be distinguished from a pulling up and down of the collarbones and shoulder blades as we breathe, another movement often substituted for the legitimate movement of breathing. Our collarbones and shoulder blades should simply remain comfortably and flexibly suspended over our moving ribs. ▨

This picture shows our lungs in the context of our whole torsos. We must understand that air goes no lower in the torso than the lungs. Very important movements of breathing happen lower than the lungs, but those lower movements must not be confused with air or with the movement of air, which flows in and out of our lungs, and no lower.

Singers do well to forego the use of the word ribcage. Cage is a terrible metaphor for ribs. The point of a cage is that the bars should not move. The point of ribs is movement. Singers do well to map their ribs as individuals, as they do their fingers. No rib is exactly like its neighbor, nor is its movement exactly like its neighbor's.

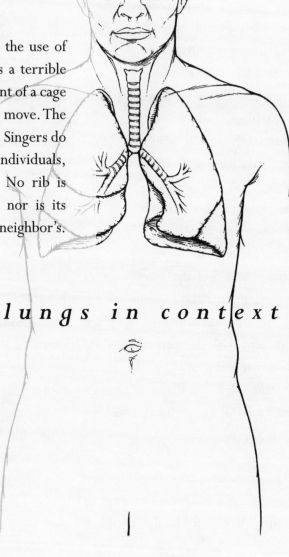

lungs in context

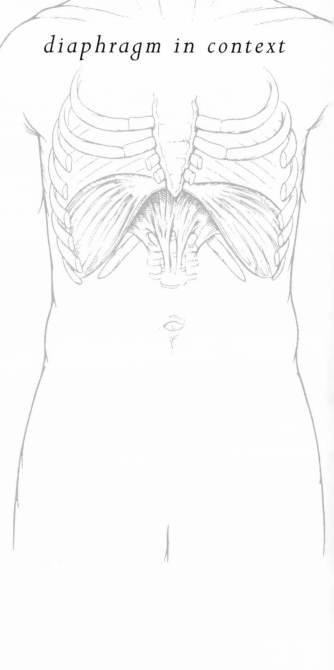

This picture shows our diaphragms in the context of our whole torsos. We must understand that our diaphragms are horizontal structures (not vertical!) which dome high in our ribs, dividing the thoracic cavity above from the abdominal and pelvic cavities below (no lower!).

In this regard, the frequent injunction to "breathe low" is confusing to young singers, not because low isn't important—it is terribly important—but because the injunction undervalues and distracts from the equally important higher movement of ribs and diaphragm. Our lungs and diaphragms lie higher in our torsos than any other organs except our hearts, which snuggle between our lungs, just above our highly domed diaphragms. Students ask, "Should we breathe high or low?" The answer is yes. We should breathe high, and we should breathe middle, and we should breathe low, across the whole natural range of breathing movement. Fine singing depends on movement choices throughout the entire torso. ▨

Ribs have their excursion in breathing, and the diaphragm has its excursion. The excursion of the diaphragm takes it from a highly domed position to a less domed position, thereby increasing the diameter of the thorax on inhalation. On exhalation the diaphragm returns to its highly domed position in preparation for its next excursion downward and outward. Just as the ribs must make their full excursion down and in, so must the diaphragm make its full excursion to fully domed if breathing is to be perfect for singing.

In the diaphragm, movement receptors are sparse compared to their density in the limbs and trunk, so singers need to sense the diaphragm's working chiefly by its effects in the movement of abdominal vicera and the pelvic floor. This can be compared to sensing the working of the heart by feeling the pulse.

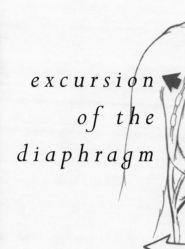

excursion of the diaphragm

Breathing is a wave-like movement from top to bottom, both on inhalation and on exhalation. On inhalation, the ribs swing up and out, the diaphragm descends, the abdominal and pelvic viscera (a.k.a. organs, gut, entrails, innards) are moved outward and downward by the powerful descending diaphragm, and the pelvic floor is pushed downward by the pressure of the displaced viscera.

On exhalation, the ribs swing down and in, the diaphragm ascends, the abdominal and pelvic viscera flow inward and upward as the diaphragm ascends and the cylinder of abdominal musculature springs back inward as the pressure from the viscera is gradually reduced; the pelvic floor likewise springs back to its neutral position.

The movement of the diaphragm creates a kind of tide in the viscera, essential to health. When the tide is reduced by improper breathing due to

disease or tension people are more susceptible to abdominal and pelvic infection. Some people imagine it is bad for our organs to be perpetually moved. Actually, it is good for them!

The movement of breathing is sequential, and it is also unified, or coordinated, in a way that makes it feel like a single movement top to bottom when we are free of tension. In this regard the movement of breathing is like all other movement in tension-free bodies, both sequential and coordinated.

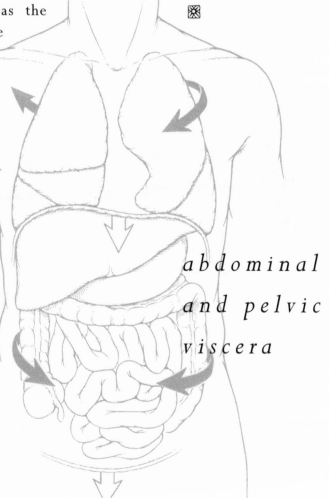

abdominal and pelvic viscera

On these two pages are the anterior abdominal wall (in front) and the posterior abdominal wall (in back). Singers who think of the abdominal wall only in front cheat themselves by half and misconceive abdominal movement in breathing. Our abdominal wall is a layered cylinder of muscle surrounding our viscera, front, sides, and back. The pressure put on the abdominal wall by the viscera's being moved outward and downward by the descending diaphragm is equal in all directions. The viscera do not selectively press against the anterior abdominal wall at the expense of the sides and back. The viscera move outward against the entire cylinder, and the movement should be felt all around, not just in front. This is another instance of "breathing into the back," to which we should add "breathing into the sides." ※

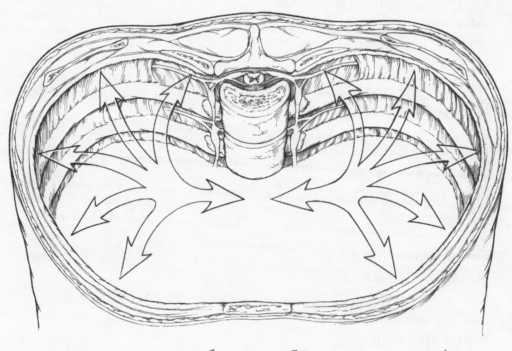

abdominal wall in front

The viscera meet some resistance in our backs and sides that they do not meet in front, where there is no bone except the pubis. Here at our backs and sides our viscera meet the resistance of our pelvic bones and our spines. The viscera will not, however, meet resistance from lower ribs if the the lower ribs are being allowed their full excursion.

The fact that there is resistance in the bony portions of the posterior abdominal wall does not mean that there will not be movement. There is much movement where there is no bone, and subtler movement occurs in the pelvis and spine in breathing. The fact that there is resistance in the posterior abdominal wall does not mean that there will not be sensation. These bony areas are lined with tactile and kinesthetic sensors, and sensation in this area is profound in breathing, particularly the sensation of pressure against the pelvic bones on inhalation and the engagement of our deep pelvic structures on exhalation as our spines lengthen. ▨

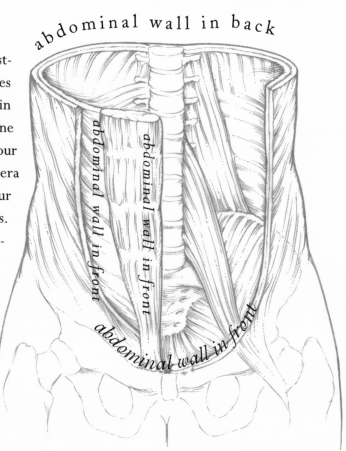

abdominal wall in back

abdominal wall in front

abdominal wall in front

abdominal wall in front

Singers need a very clear distinction in their Body Maps between the muscles interior to the pelvis and the muscles exterior to the pelvis. The interior muscles are continuous with the base of the diaphragm and are powerfully experienced in tension-free singing, not as work, but as movement, engagement, activity, dynamic support, potent responsiveness, energy, vigor, aliveness, fire. Successful singers often resort to metaphor, like energy, or fire, or support, to describe this lively interior feeling and to distinguish it from work.

The freer and more buoyant singing is on the inside of the pelvis, the more likely it is that there will be a sensation of release or spreading or dropping throughout the gluteal system, exterior to the pelvis, on exhalation. This sensation is not to be confused with "tucking." Tucking is work, and it interferes with the releasing sensation, rather than facilitating it. What facilitates it is the clear mapping of muscles exterior to the pelvis as distinguished from those interior.

Interior to the pelvis we experience an upward flow of support for the ascending diaphragm, and exterior to the pelvis we feel a downward and outward release. This is complex, but it needn't be confusing. Singers are accustomed to complex sensation of movement in anatomically separate structures in multiple directions, such as the jaw dropping as the palate rises, or the ribs swinging down and in as the diaphragm ascends, the spine lengthening in a felt upward direction as the weight delivery into the floor through the bony structure provides a downward grounding or anchoring. ▨

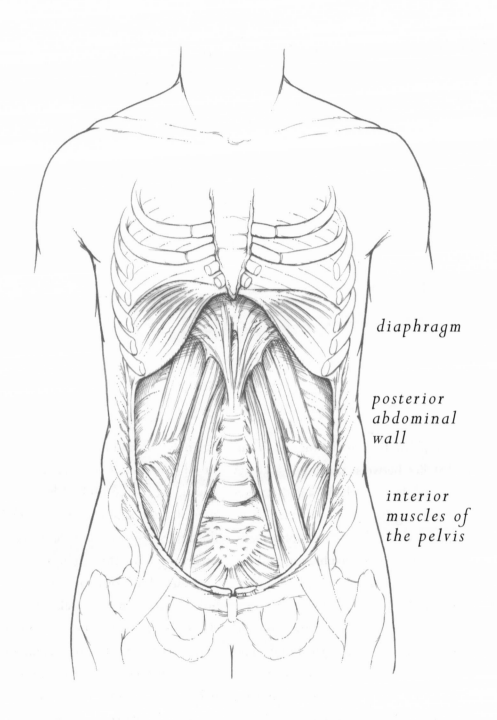

diaphragm

posterior
abdominal
wall

interior
muscles of
the pelvis

pelvic floor / pelvic diaphragm

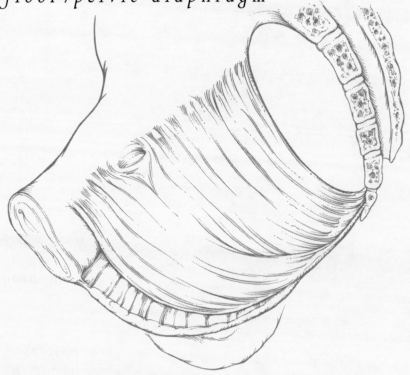

The pelvic floor is the muscle group that lies between the pubis and the sacrum front to back and between the sitting bones side to side. These muscles are often metaphorically called the pelvic diaphragm, and the metaphor is valid to a certain point, inspired by the domed shape (inverted, of course) and the importance of the movement in breathing. The metaphor breaks down on the matter of work. Our thoracic diaphragm works when we inhale, and our pelvic "diaphragm" must not work. If our pelvic floor muscles work (as in Kegel exercises, for instance) as we inhale, we compromise the excursion of the diaphragm; if our pelvic floor muscles work on exhalation we interfere with the springing back to neutral of our pelvic floors. Sometimes singers believe they should exercise the pelvic floor so that it can work on exhalation. Rather, singers should exercise their pelvic floor so that the muscles are toned and capable of springing back to neutral on exhalation. ▨

As the diaphragm descends it pushes hard on all the viscera that lie between the diaphragm and the pelvic floor. The viscera are pushed outward against the abdominal wall, but they are also pushed downward against the pelvic floor where they do not meet the kind of resistance they meet at the pelvic bones. Therefore, the pelvic floor descends as the diaphragm descends (unless it's tightening). When the diaphragm ascends the pelvic diaphragm ascends because the pressure from the viscera is taken off it. In this way, the pelvic diaphragm and the abdominal wall are similar in their response to the ascending diaphragm. This springing back of the abdominal wall and the pelvic floor is a dynamic, lively sensation, to be distinguished from the sensation of work in these areas. Voluntary work in these areas interferes with their natural involuntary action. Tone is a good word to

the coordination of movement of the two diaphragms

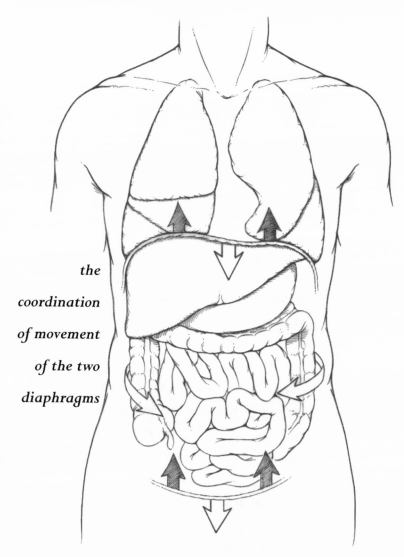

describe what we want to feel in these muscles, tone being the firmness and dynamic character proper to the tissues of our bodies. ▨

Just as body awareness and Body Mapping provide the context for singing technique, so the spine provides the context, within our Body Maps, for the singing structures. In fact, because the action of the spine is so important for breathing, the spine itself might rightly be regarded as a singing structure.

The spine is the context for our singing structures because the singing structures lie along the entire length of the weight-bearing spine, and beyond. The oral pharynx and the laryngeal pharynx are just forward of cervical vertebrae; only the esophagus lies between the trachea and vertebrae; the back half of each lung lies alongside our spine; the diaphragm anchors firmly onto lumbar vertebrae, and the deep inner pelvic muscles that are continuous with the base of the diaphragm fan out from alongside lumbar vertebrae. It is as if the singing structures snuggled as close as they could get to their supporting spine at every location along the length of the spine.

Singers need to map their singing structures in relation to the spine, not in isolation from it. One consequence of this happy mapping of structures in relation to each other is the reduction or elimination of bodily tension. A breathing mechanism supported along its whole length by a massive spine does not require effort to hold it up. ▓

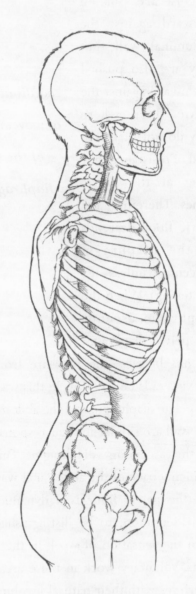

spine

The spine is the context for our singing structures for another reason: the spine's movement is a crucial part of the movement of breathing. When the spine's natural movement in breathing is interfered with, singing is not dynamic or buoyant, and singers compensate for the loss of buoyancy with effort. The spine's natural movement in singing is to lengthen and gather. The spine lengthens on exhalation, and it gathers on inhalation.

The lengthening and gathering of the spine in breathing is involuntary. We don't need to do it; nature does it for us. We do, however, need to cooperate with it, and we certainly need not to interfere with it.

The spine's gathering on inhalation facilitates the excursion of the ribs up and out and it facilitates the excursion of the diaphragm. The spine's lengthening on exhalation facilitates the return movements of the ribs and diaphragm. The lengthening and gathering of the spine in breathing achieves even more for singers; it activates the deep sensations of breathing that come from the pelvis. If we prevent our spinal lengthening by the tension of "standing up straight" or of slouching, then the pelvis remains inert in our experience of exhalation. The pelvic liveliness so prized by fine singers is sadly missing. Fortunately, even if pelvic liveliness has been compromised in the past, it can be recovered. ❊

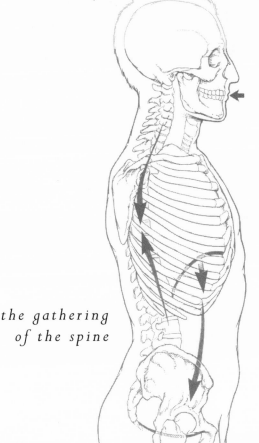

the gathering of the spine

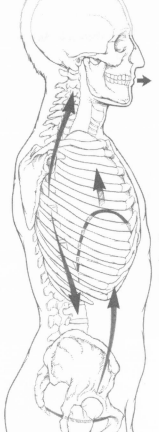

and the lengthening of the spine

Our heads are also context for our singing structures because of the head's relationship to the spine. Our heads balance on our top vertebra, called the atlas, in such a way that they are in constant play in relation to the spine, subtly altering their poise at every moment of singing depending on the musical character of the moment. This dynamic play of the skull on the spine is discernible even when there are large gestures of the head and spine. There is small movement and large movement at the same time.

Singing is a particular instance of a general principle: in verte-brate movement the head leads and the body follows, or, the head leads and the spine follows. We may observe this phenome-non in fine dancers, fine athletes, in toddlers, in race horses, and in our cats, as they jump or stretch or begin to move out of their resting positions. We may observe it also in singers who are free

of tension and beautifully balanced, whose dynamically balanced heads lead their spinal lengthening and their broader spinal gestures, like turning or bending.

Some singers fix their heads on their spines in a misguided attempt at con-trol. These singers need to redefine control so that their control is dynamic rather than rigid. Dynamic control is a finer, more reliable con-trol than rigid control. ✠

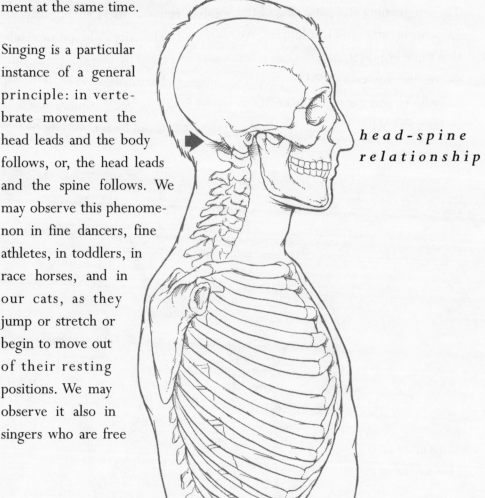

head-spine relationship

A very important feature of the play of the head in relation to the top vertebra is a slight movement toward the spine as the spine gathers and a slight movement away from the spine as the spine lengthens. This slight moving away has been called "up and over" by many technique teachers; it was called "forward and up" by F.M. Alexander as he liberated it in his own reciting of Shakespeare. Unless the "up and over" is allowed in experience, the spine will not lengthen as it should on exhalation, and labored breathing results.

"Up and over" can be seen, when we have developed eyes for it, and it can be felt, with our increasingly sophisticated and sensitive kinesthetic receptors in the joints of our heads with our spines. "Up and over" is felt as buoyancy, described by singers sometimes as "space in the joint," or "a little balloon between my skull and my spine," or "a sort of nodding toward the stars," or "a making room for the breath." Again, when there is metaphor, we want to find the anatomical basis for the metaphor and secure the movement that inspires the metaphor. ▨

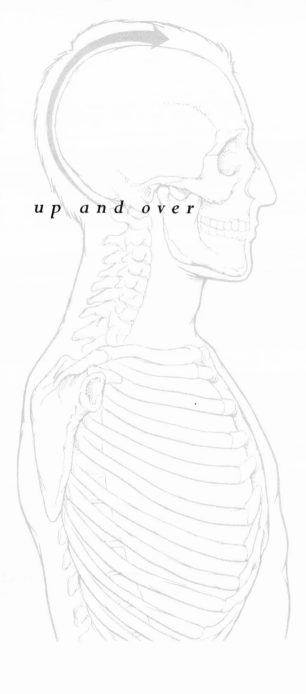

up and over

superficial

muscles of

the neck

Perfect balance of the head on the spine in singing, and the subtle play of the head on the spine in singing, and the all-important involuntary "up and over" of the head in relation to the top vertebra in singing, all these depend on freedom in the large muscles of the neck. These large muscles are not singing muscles. They are head-moving muscles, and, as such, are purely gestural in singing, moving the head here or there.

Singers must learn control, a particular kind of control, the kind that comes from neurons. The control that comes from neurons, the cells of our nervous system, involves attention, intention, and moment by moment choice. A singer's learned skill is inclusive attention (oneself and one's surroundings), sufficient intention (a clear conception of the movement of singing and the ability to carry it out), and proper choices (muscular freedom, non-interference, and active cooperation with the involuntary aspects of singing). Tense singers try to control with muscle fibers what they should be controlling with neurons. We should think of singing as brain work, first, muscle work, second. ▨

Singers need a very complete map of the neck, since freedom in singing depends first, last, and always on freedom in neck muscles. Singers need to map the full depth of their necks, from the base of the skull at the top to the collarbones at the bottom. Singers need to map the whole cylinder of neck muscles, back, sides

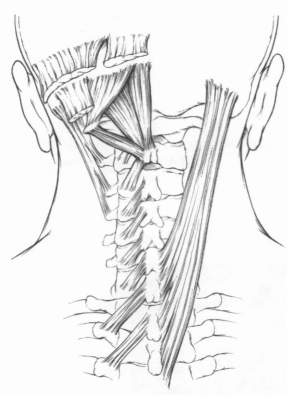

deep muscles of the neck

and front, including muscles that lie within the hyoid bone and muscles that attach to the lower rim of the (single) jaw. Singers need also to map the muscles' layering, from superficial muscles to deep muscles, because the action of these deep muscles in singing must not be interfered with by the tightening of the superficial muscles.

We must understand that, in terms of the geography of the body, singing is profoundly interior. There is a wonderful convergence in the centrality or interiority or coreness of singing in our human body and our human spirit, since we experience singing as coming from "deep within" emotionally and intellectually. Singing is deeply integrative of body and spirit in another way, as well. As singers achieve mastery, their conception of the music and their conception of the movement that manifests the music arise within them simultaneously. This is a happy condition indeed, dependent on excellent singing technique and also dependent on the context for technique: lively body awareness, good Body Maps, and free, buoyant bodies. ▨

About the Author

Barbara Conable is teacher, trainer, writer, prize-winning poet, grandmother, gardener, and cook, living in Portland, Oregon.

She is founder and president of Andover Educators, a network of musicians saving, securing, and enhancing musical careers with accurate information about the body in movement.

Barbara is a teaching member of the North American Society of the Teachers of the Alexander Technique and of Alexander Technique International.

Barbara is also the author of the highly acclaimed *How to Learn the Alexander Technique: A Manual for Students* and of *What Every Musician Needs to Know about the Body: The Practical Application of Body Mapping to Making Music.*

Barbara continues to train Andover Educators, write books, and develop the theory and practice of Body Mapping in Portland, Oregon.

Barbara Conable

About the Illustrator

Tim Phelps, CMI, Associate Professor and Medical Illustrator, teaches and illustrates in the Department of Art as Applied to Medicine at Johns Hopkins in Baltimore, MD. In the creation of art for a number of individuals and firms, Tim has received numerous regional and national awards. His work has been published in textbooks, magazines and professional journals and has been displayed in over 35 group and solo exhibitions. Recent work includes principal illustrator for the *Johns Hopkins Family Health Book*, the Smithsonian's *Ocean Planet,* a traveling exhibit, and coauthorship of *Surgical Pathology Dissection: An Illustrated Guide,* receiving the Best Illustrated Book Award from the Association of Medical Illustrators in 1996. Tim was also a featured artist in *American Artist* magazine in 1997. The American Urological Association awarded him the William P. Didusch Art Award in 1998.

James Jordan

One of America's most respected choral conductors and educators, James Jordan is conductor of the Westminster Chapel Choir and associate professor of conducting at Westminster Choir College in Princeton, NJ. James Jordan is author of *The Musician's Soul* (1999) and *Evoking Sound* (1996), published by GIA.

James Jordan

Index

A

Abdominal wall, 11, 33-35, 39, *See also* Viscera
　　illustration, 34, 35, 37
Alignment, 8, 11
　　alignment reminders, 10
Awareness, 9, 13-14, 27
　　awareness reminders, 9-10
　　inclusive, 13
　　kinesthetic sensors, 13, 18, 35, 43
　　tactile sensors, 13, 17-18, 35

B

Balance, 15
　　skeletal balance (illustration), 15
Body mapping, 8, 13
Breathing
　　breathing reminders, 10-11
　　illustration, 33
　　process, 28-30, 33, 41

C

Control, 44

D

Diaphragm, 11, 24, 31-33, 38-39, 40-41
　　coordination of movement, 39
　　　　illustration, 39
　　excursion of (illustration), 32
　　illustration, 31, 37
　　pelvic, 38-39. *See also* Pelvis

E

Esophagus, 10, 23-24, 40
　　illustration, 25
Excursion
　　ribs, 28, 32, 41
　　diaphragm, 32, 41
Exhalation, 11, 24, 28, 32-33, 35-36, 38,
　　41, 43

F

Facial muscles, 20-21. *See also* Lips
　　illustration, 21

H

Head, 10, 42-44
　　in relation to spine (illustration), 42

I

Inhalation, 11, 16, 23-24, 28, 32-33, 35, 38,
　　41

J

Jaw, 19

L

Lips, 22
　　illustration, 22
Lungs, 11, 26-27, 30-31, 40
　　illustration, 26, 27, 30

M

Mouth, 16-17
　　illustration, 17

N

Nasal passage, 16
　　illustration, 16
Neck, 44-45
　　deep muscles of (illustration), 45
　　superficial muscles of (illustration), 44

P

Palate, 20
Pelvis, 33, 35-36, 38-39, 40-41, *See also* Viscera
　　interior muscles (illustration), 37
　　pelvic floor/pelvic diaphragm (illustration), 38
Pharynx, 23, 40
　　muscles of (illustration), 23

R

Ribs, 10, 26, 31, 33, 41
　　illustration, 28, 29
　　movement, 28-30

S

Spine, 10-11, 15, 28, 35, 40-43
　　gathering of (illustration), 41
　　illustration, 40
　　lengthening of (illustration), 41
　　Up and Over, 10
　　　　illustration, 43

T

Temporo-mandibular joint, 19
　　illustration, 19
Tongue, 17, 18
　　illustration, 18
Trachea, 10, 24, 40
　　illustration, 25

U

Up and Over, *See* Spine

V

Viscera, abdominal and pelvic (illustration), 33